HOME ORGANIST LIBRARY VOLUME 33

Irish Songs

Arranged by Kenneth Baker.

This publication is not authorised for sale in the
United States of America and/or Canada.

Wise Publications
London/New York/Paris/Sydney/Copenhagen/Madrid

Exclusive Distributors:
Music Sales Limited
8/9 Frith Street, London W1V 5TZ, England.
Music Sales Pty Limited
120 Rothschild Avenue, Rosebery, NSW 2018, Australia.

Order No. AM937222
ISBN 0-7119-5782-7
This book © Copyright 1997 by Wise Publications

Compiled by Peter Evans
Music arranged by Kenneth Baker
Music processed by MSS Studios

Cover design by Studio Twenty, London

Printed in the United Kingdom by
Caligraving Limited, Thetford, Norfolk.

Your Guarantee of Quality
As publishers, we strive to produce every book to
the highest commercial standards.
The music has been freshly engraved and the book has
been carefully designed to minimise awkward page turns
and to make playing from it a real pleasure.
Particular care has been given to specifying acid-free, neutral-sized
paper made from pulps which have not been elemental chlorine bleached.
This pulp is from farmed sustainable forests and
was produced with special regard for the environment.
Throughout, the printing and binding have been planned to ensure a
sturdy, attractive publication which should give years of enjoyment.
If your copy fails to meet our high standards, please inform us
and we will gladly replace it.

Music Sales' complete catalogue describes thousands of titles and is
available in full colour sections by subject, direct from Music Sales Limited.
Please state your areas of interest and send a cheque/postal order
for £1.50 for postage to: Music Sales Limited, Newmarket Road,
Bury St. Edmunds, Suffolk IP33 3YB.

Visit the Internet Music Shop at
http://www.musicsales.co.uk

Mother Machree

Words & Music by Rida Johnson Young, Chauncy Olcott & Ernest R. Ball

Upper: oboe
Lower: flutes
Pedal: 16' + 8'
Drums: waltz

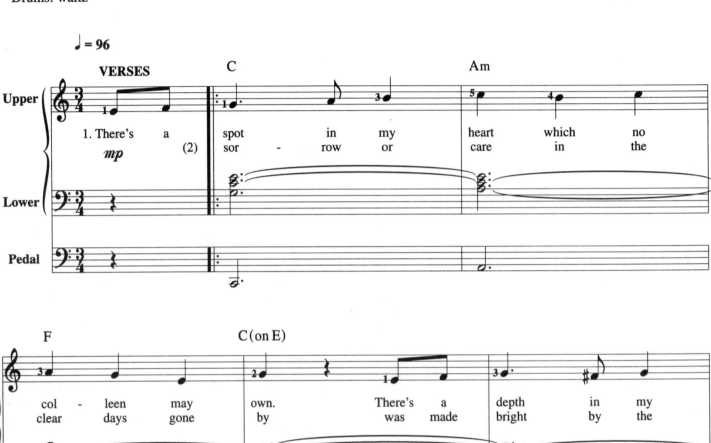

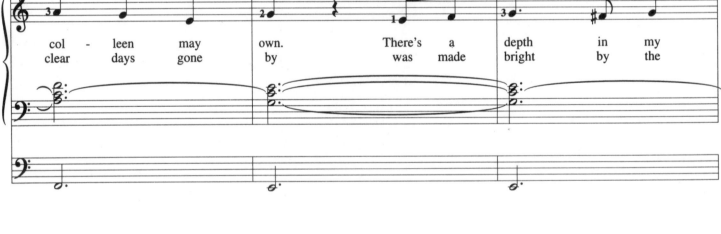

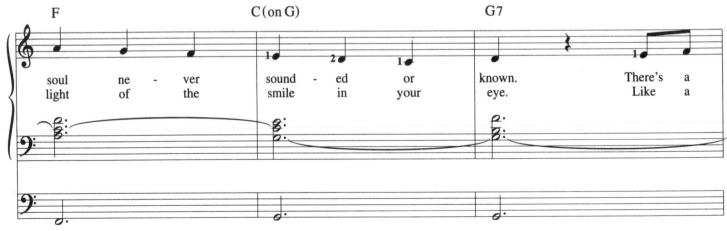

The Spinning Wheel

Words & Music by John Francis Waller & Delia Murphy

Upper: harp
Lower: flutes + piano
Pedal: 8'
Drums: slow rock

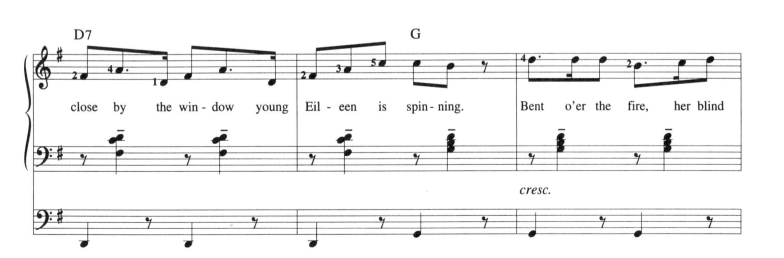

(stop drums last time)

2. "Eileen, a chara*, I hear someone tapping, "
   "'Tis the ivy, dear mother, against the glass flapping."
   "Eily, I surely hear somebody sighing,"
   "'Tis the sound, mother dear, of the autumn winds dying."
   Merrily, cheerily, noisily whirring *(etc.)*

3. "What's that noise that I hear at the window I wonder?"
   "'Tis the little birds chirping the holly-bush under."
   "What makes you be pushing and moving your stool on?"
   "And singing all wrong that old song of Coolin?"
   Merrily, cheerily, noisily whirring *(etc.)*

4. There's a form at the casement, the form of her true love,
   And he whispers with face bent, "I'm waiting for you, love.
   "Get up on the stool, through the lattice step lightly,
   "And we'll rove in the grove while the moon's shining brightly."
   Merrily, cheerily, noisily whirring *(etc.)*

5. The maid shakes her head, on her lips lays her fingers,
   Steals up from the seat, longs to go and yet lingers.
   A frightened glance turns to her drowsy grandmother,
   Puts one foot on the stool, spins the wheel with the other.
   Merrily, cheerily, noisily whirring *(etc.)*

6. Lazily, easily, swings now the wheel round,
   Slowly and lowly is heard now the reel's sound.
   Noiseless and light to the lattice above her,
   The maid steps, then leaps to the arms of her lover.
   Slower, and slower, and slower the wheel swings.
   Lower, and lower, and lower the reel rings.
   Ere the reel and the wheel stopped their spinning and moving,
   Through the grove the young lovers by moonlight are roving.

   * pronounced KAURA

Rose Of Tralee

Words & Music by E. M. Spencer & C. W. Glover

Upper: piano
Lower: flutes
Pedal: 16' + 8'
Drums: waltz

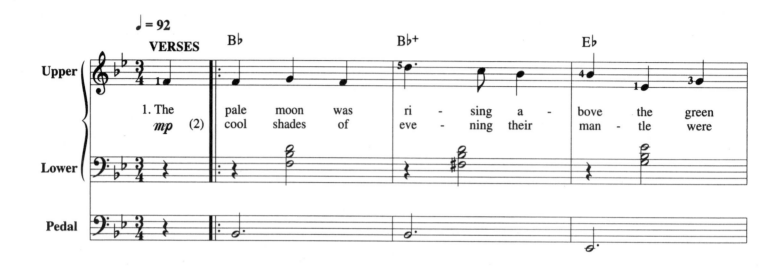

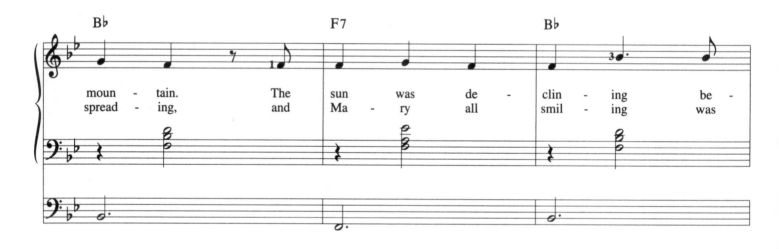

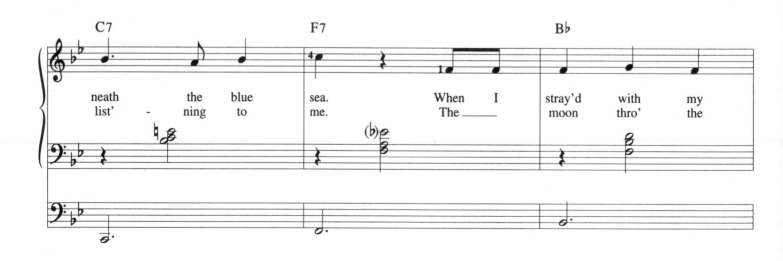

The Garden Where The Praties Grow

Words & Music by Johnny Patterson

Upper: flute
Lower: flutes
Pedal: 16' + 8'
Drums: swing

2.
Says I, "My pretty Kathleen, I'm tired of single life,
And if you've no objection, sure, I'll make you my sweet wife."
She answered me right modestly, and curtsied very low,
"Oh, you're welcome to the garden where the praties grow."
　　She was just the sort of creature, boys, *(etc.)*

3.
Says I, "My pretty Kathleen, I hope that you'll agree,"
She was not like your city girls who say you're making free.
Says she, "I'll ask my parents and tomorrow I'll let you know,
If you'll meet me in the garden where the praties grow."
　　She was just the sort of creature, boys, *(etc.)*

4.
O the parents they consented, and we're blest with children three
Two boys just like their mother, and a girl the image of me.
And now we're goin' to train them up the way they ought to go,
For to dig in the garden where the praties grow.
　　She was just the sort of creature, boys, *(etc.)*

Father O'Flynn

Words by A. P. Graves
Music Traditional. Adapted by C. Villiers Stanford

Upper: trumpet
Lower: flutes + piano
Pedal: 16' + 8'
Drums: march 6/8 (or swing)

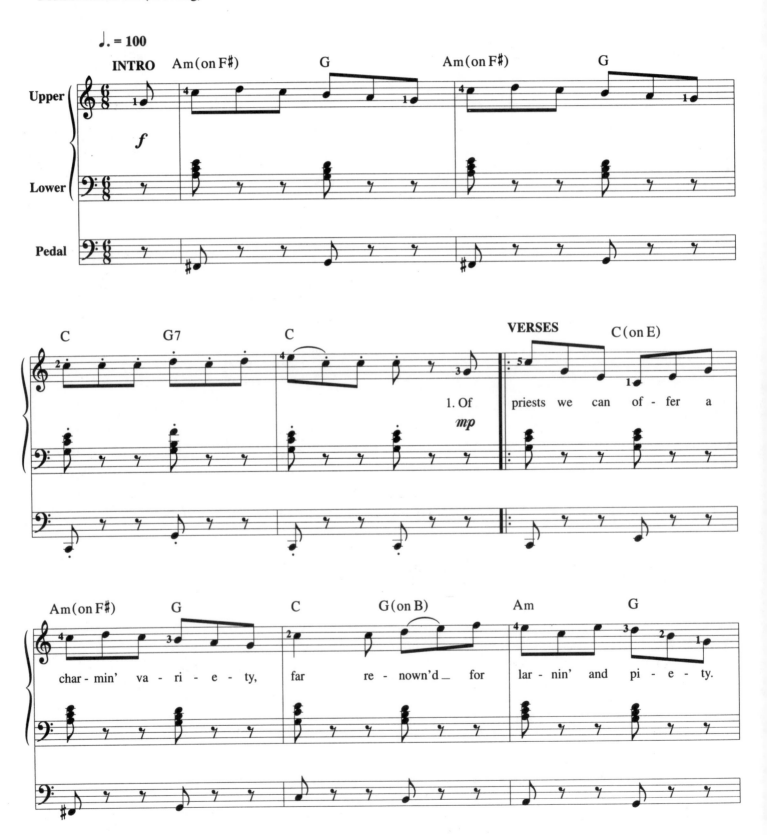

* "your health"

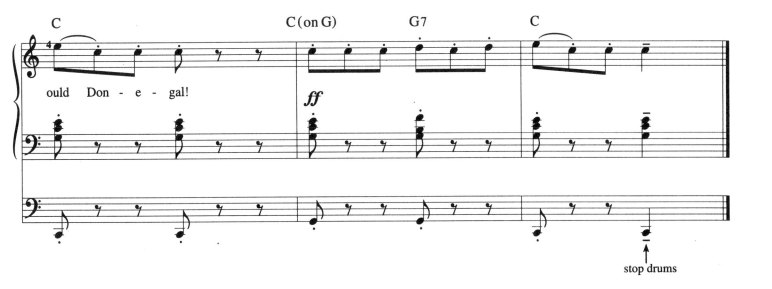

ould Don - e - gal!

ff

stop drums

2. Don't talk of your Provost and Fellows of Trinity,
   Famous forever at Greek and Latinity.
   Dad and the divils, and all at Divinity,
   Father O'Flynn would make hares of them all.

Bridge. Come, I venture to give ye my word,
   Never the likes of his logic was heard.
   Down from mythology, into thayology,
   Troth! And conchology, if he'd the call!

3. Och! Father O'Flynn you've a wonderful way wid you.
   All ould sinners are wishful to pray wid you.
   All the young childer are wild for to play wid you,
   You've such a way wid you, Father avick.

Bridge. Still for all you've so gentle a soul.
   Glad you've your flock in the grandest control.
   Checking the crazy ones, coaxin' onaisy ones,
   Lifting the lazy ones on wid the stick.

4. And tho' quite avoidin' all foolish frivolity,
   Still at all seasons of innocent jollity.
   Where was the play-boy could claim an equality
   At comicality, Father, wid you?

Bridge. Once the Bishop look'd grave at your jest,
   Till this remark set him off wid the rest:
   "Is it lave gaiety, all to the laity?
   Cannot the clergy be Irishmen too?"

Final Chorus. Here's a health to you, Father O'Flynn.
   Slainté and slainté and slainté agin.
   Pow'rfullest preacher and tinderest teacher,
   And kindliest creature in ould Donegal!

The Mountains Of Mourne

Words & Music by Percy French & Houston Collisson

Upper: clarinet
Lower: flutes
Pedal: 16' + 8'
Drums: waltz

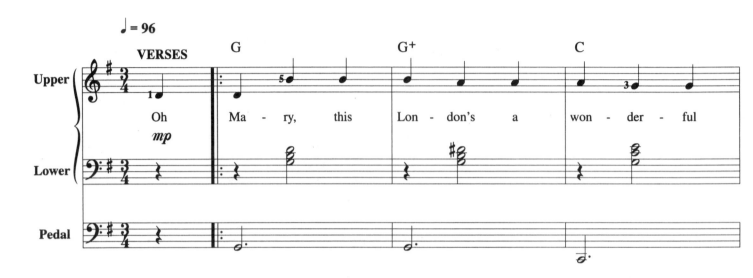

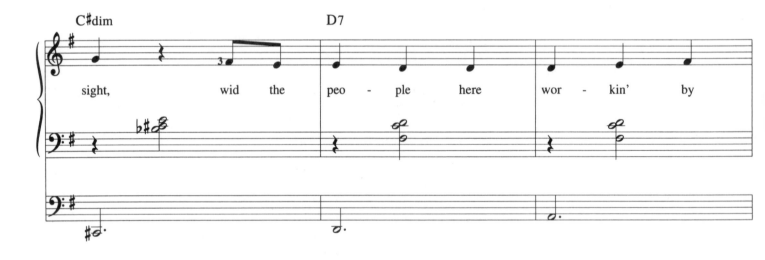

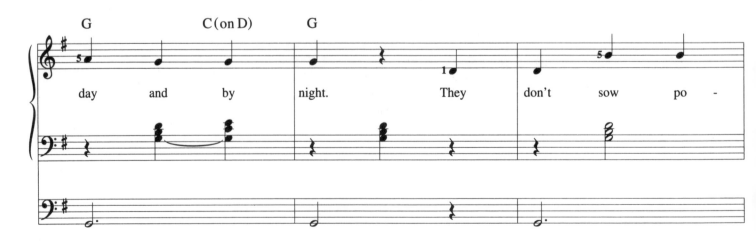

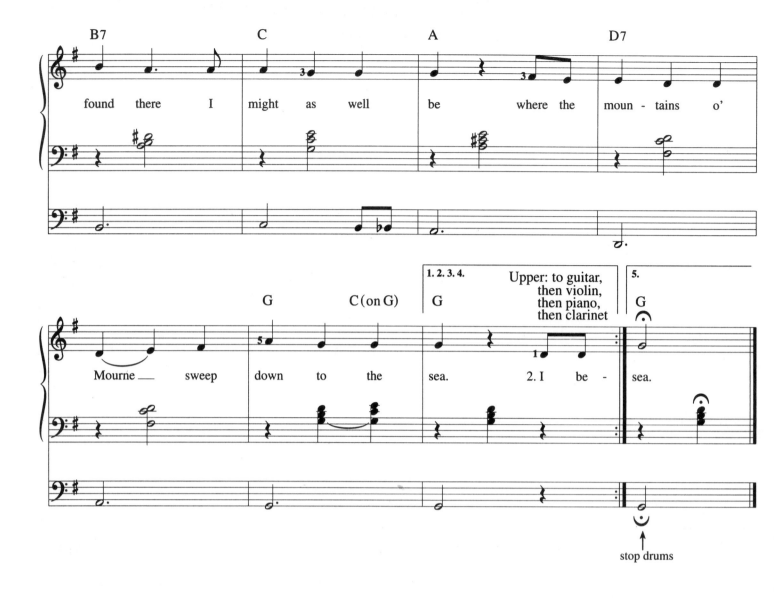

2. I believe that when writin', a wish you expressed
   As to how the fine ladies in London were dressed.
   Well if you'll believe me, when asked to a ball,
   Faith, they don't wear a top to their dresses at all.
   Oh, I've seen them meself, and you could not, in thrath,
   Say if they were bound for a ball or a bath.
   Don't be startin' them fashions now, Mary Macree,
   Where the mountains o' Mourne sweep down to the sea.

3. I've seen England's King from the top of a bus,
   I never knew him, tho' he means to know us.
   And tho' by the Saxon we once were oppressed,
   Still I cheered (God forgive me), I cheered with the rest.
   And now that he's visited Erin's green shore,
   We'll be much better friends than we've been heretofore.
   When we've got all we want we're as quiet as can be
   Where the mountains o' Mourne sweep down to the sea.

4. You remember young Peter O'Loughlin, of course?
   Well now he is here at the head o' the force.
   I met him today, I was crossin' The Strand,
   And he stopped the whole street wid wan wave of his hand.
   And there we stood talking of days that are gone,
   While the whole population of London looked on.
   But for all these great powers he's wishful, like me,
   To be back where dark Mourne sweeps down to the sea.

5. There's beautiful girls here, oh, niver mind.
   Wid beautiful shapes nature niver designed.
   And lovely complexions all roses and crame,
   But O'Loughlin remarked wid regard to the same.
   "That if those roses you venture to sip,
   The colours might all come away on your lip."
   So I'll wait for the wild rose that's waitin' for me,
   Where the mountains of Mourne sweep down to the sea.

The Town I Loved So Well

Words & Music by Phil Coulter

Upper: piano
Lower: flutes
Pedal: bass guitar
Drums: 8 beat

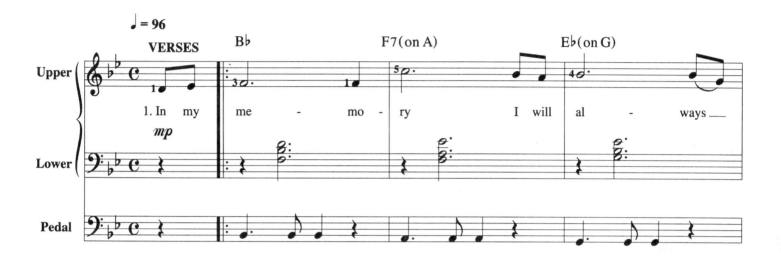

1. In my me - mo - ry I will al - ways

see the town that I have loved so

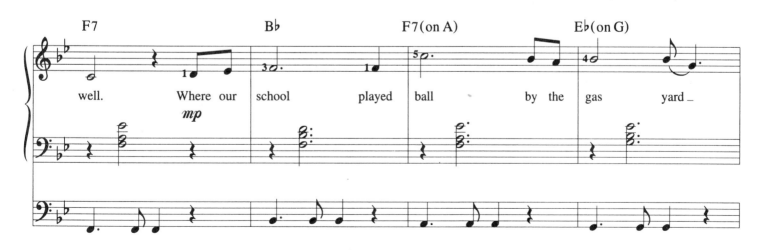

well. Where our school played ball by the gas yard

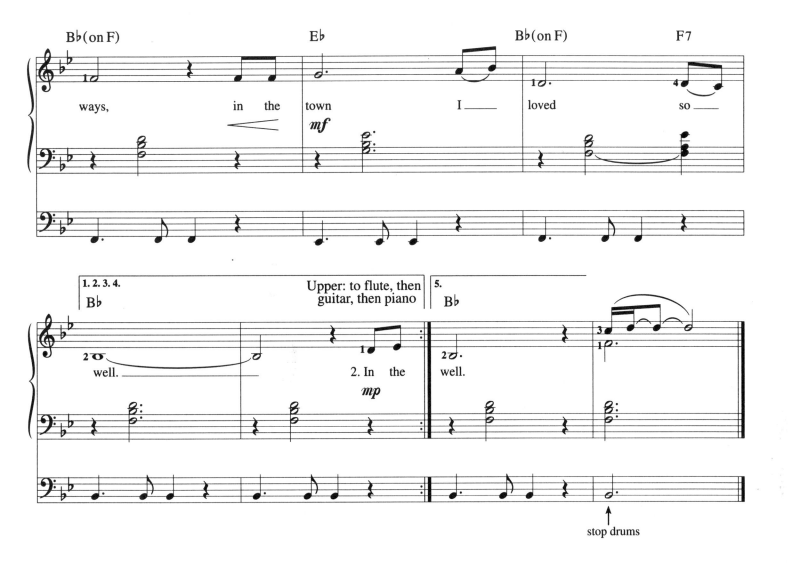

stop drums

2. In the early morning the shirt factory horn
   Called women from Creggan, the Moor, and the Bog.
   While the men on the dole played a mother's role:
   Fed the children and then walked the dog.
   And when times got tough there was just about enough,
   And they saw it through without complaining.
   For deep inside was a burning pride
   In the town I loved so well.

3. There was music there in the Derry air,
   Like a language that we all could understand.
   I remember the day that I earned my first pay,
   When I played in a small pick-up band.
   There I spent my youth, and to tell you the truth,
   I was sad to leave it all behind me,
   For I'd learned about life, and I'd found a wife,
   In the town I loved so well.

4. But when I've returned how my eyes have burned
   To see how a town could be brought to its knees
   By the armoured cars and the bombed-out bars,
   And the gas that hangs on to every breeze.
   Now the army's installed by that old gas yard wall,
   And damned barbed wire gets higher and higher,
   With their tanks and their guns, oh my God, what have they done
   To the town I loved so well?

5. Now the music's gone, but they carry on,
   For their spirit's bruised, never broken.
   They will not forget, but their hearts are set
   On tomorrow, and peace once again.
   For what's done is done, and what's won is won,
   And what's lost is lost and gone forever,
   I can only pray for a bright brand new day,
   In the town I love so well.

Whistling Gypsy (The Gypsy Rover)

Words & Music by Leo Maguire

Upper: flute
Lower: flutes
Pedal: bass guitar
Drums: 8 beat

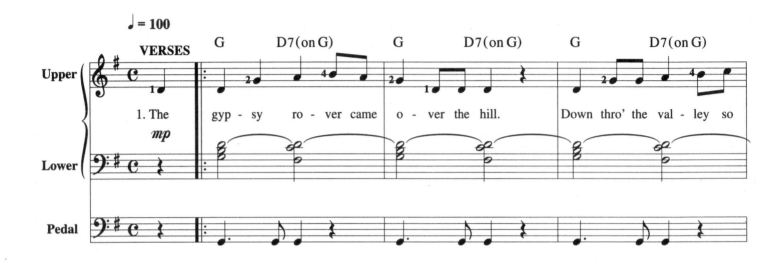

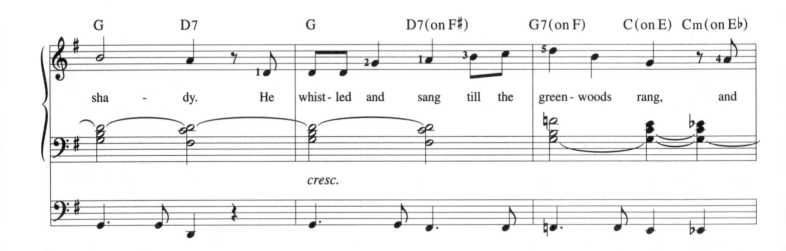

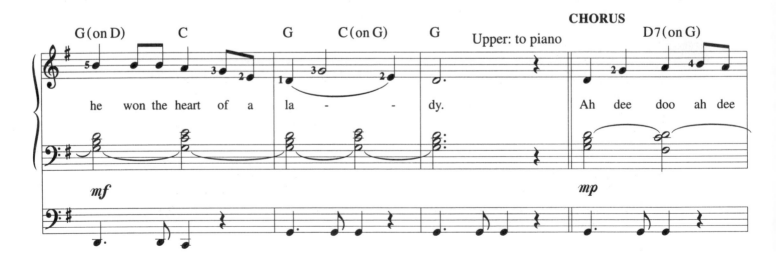

2. She left her father's castle gate,
   She left her fair young lover,
   She left her servants and her state,
   To follow the gypsy rover.
      (CHORUS)

3. Her father saddled up his fastest steed,
   He ranged the valleys over,
   He sought his daughter at great speed,
   And the whistling gypsy rover.
      (CHORUS)

4. He came at last to a mansion fine,
   Down by the river Clady,
   And there was music, and there was wine,
   For the gypsy and his lady.
      (CHORUS)

5. "He is no gypsy, father dear,
   But lord of these lands all over,
   I'm going to stay 'till my dying day,
   With my whistling gypsy rover."
      (CHORUS)

I'll Take You Home Again Kathleen

Words & Music by Thomas P. Westendorf

Upper: violin
Lower: flutes
Pedal: 16' + 8'
Drums: 8 beat

If You Ever Go To Ireland

Words & Music by Art Noel

Upper: accordion
Lower: flute
Pedal: 16' + 8'
Drums: waltz

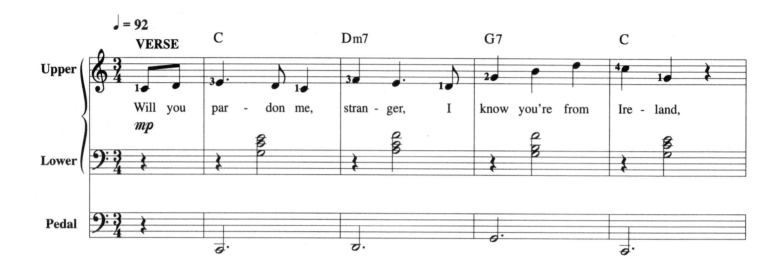

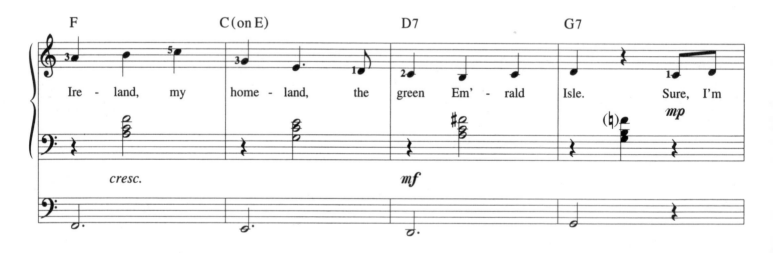

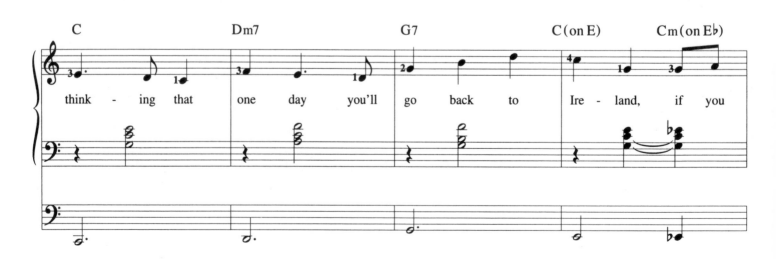

The Kerry Dance

Words & Music by James L. Molloy

Upper: flute
Lower: flutes
Pedal: 8'
Drums: march 6/8 (or swing, or off)

The Irish Rover

Adapted by Pat Clancy, Tom Clancy, Liam Clancy & Tommy Makem

Upper: guitar
Lower: flutes
Pedal: bass guitar
Drums: 8 beat

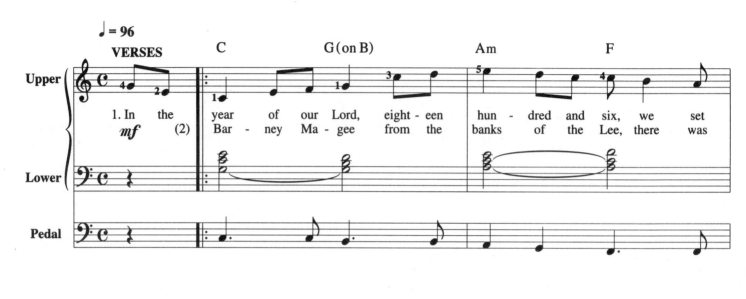

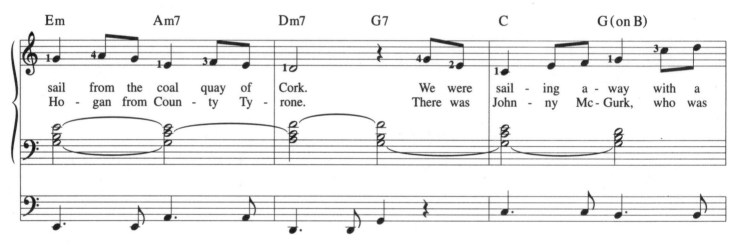

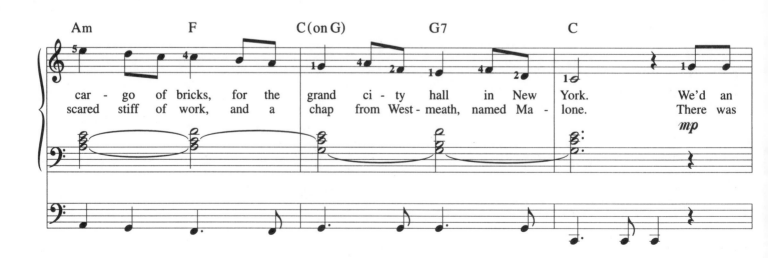

3. We had one million bags of the best Sligo rags,
   We had two million barrels of bone.
   We had three million bales of old nanny goat's tails,
   We had four million barrels of stone.
   We had five million hogs and six million dogs,
   And seven million barrels of porter.
   We had eight million sides of old blind horses' hides
   In the hold of the Irish Rover.

4. We had sailed seven years when the measels broke out,
   And our ship lost her way in a fog.
   And the whole of the crew was reduced down to two,
   'Twas myself and the captain's old dog.
   Then the ship struck a rock, O Lord, what a shock,
   And nearly tumbled over.
   Turned nine times around, then the poor dog was drowned,
   I'm the last of the Irish Rover.

Clancy Lowered The Boom

Words & Music by Hy Heath & Johnny Lange

Upper: brass ensemble
Lower: flutes + piano
Pedal: bass guitar
Drums: march 6/8 (or swing)

Cockles And Mussels

Traditional

Upper: clarinet
Lower: flutes
Pedal: 16' + 8'
Drums: waltz

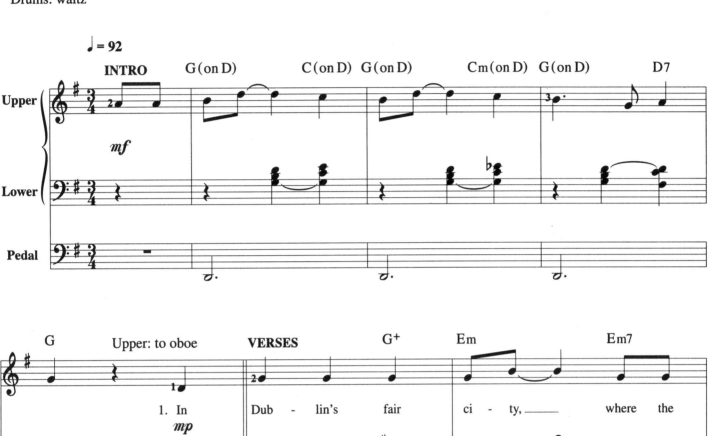

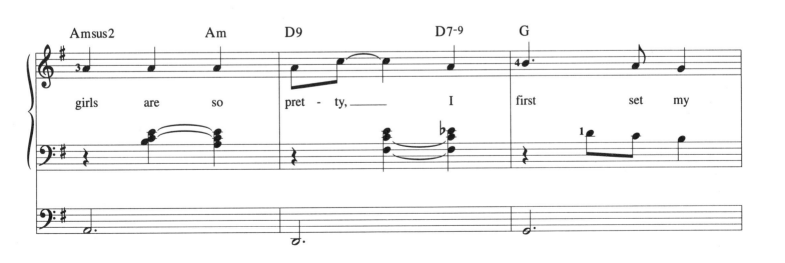

2. She was a fishmonger, but sure 'twas no wonder,
For so were her father and mother before.
And they each wheeled their barrow thro' streets broad and narrow,
Crying, "Cockles and mussels, alive alive o."
"Alive alive o!" *(etc.)*

3. She died of a fever, and no one could save her,
And that was the end of sweet Molly Malone,
Now her ghost wheels her barrow thro' streets broad and narrow,
Crying, "Cockles and mussels, alive alive o."
"Alive alive o!" *(etc.)*

Phil The Fluter

Words & Music by Percy French & David Heneker

Upper: solo flute
Lower: flutes + piano
Pedal: 8'
Drums: swing

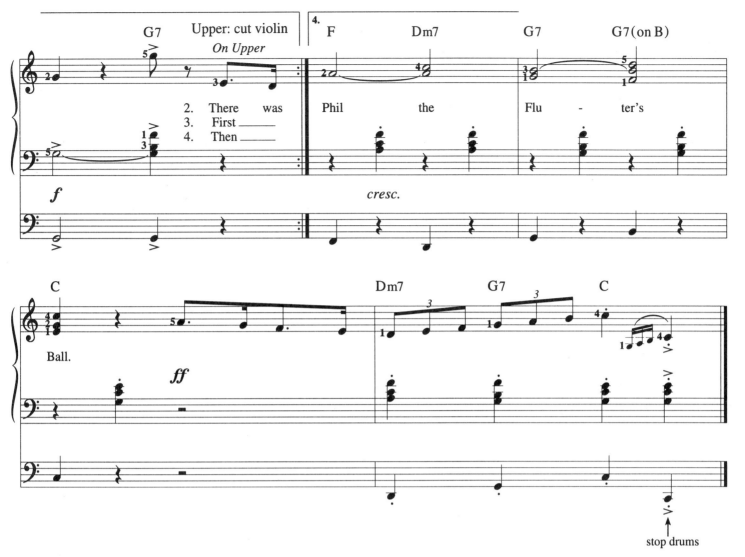

stop drums

2. There was Misther Denis Dogherty, who kept "The Runnin' Dog;"
   There was little crooked Paddy from the Tiraloughett bog.
   There were boys from ev'ry Barony, and girls from ev'ry "art,"
   And the beautiful Miss Bradys in a private ass an' cart.
   And along with them came bouncing Mrs Cafferty,
   Little Mickey Mulligan was also to the fore.
   Rose, Suzanne, and Margaret O'Rafferty,
   The flow'r of Adrumgullion and the Pride of Pethravore.
       With the toot of the flute, *(etc.)*

3. First little Micky Mulligan got up to show them how,
   And then the widow Cafferty steps out and makes her bow.
   "I could dance you off your legs," sez she, "As sure as you were born,
   "If you'll only make the piper play: 'The Hare Is In The Corn.'"
   So Phil plays up to the best of his ability,
   The lady and gentleman begin to do their share,
   While young Mick was a 'prancing with agility,
   Decrepit Mrs Cafferty was leapin' like a hare!
       With the toot of the flute, *(etc.)*

4. Then Phil the fluter tipped a wink to little crooked Pat,
   "I think it's nearly time," sez he, "For passin' round the hat"
   So Paddy did the necessary, looking mighty cute, sez
   "Ye've got to pay the piper when he toothers on the flute."
   Then all joined in wid the greatest joviality,
   Covering the Buckle and the Shuffle and the Trent.
   Jigs were danced, of the very finest quality,
   The widow found a husband, and the fluter found the rent!
       With the toot of the flute, *(etc.)*

Galway Bay

Words & Music by Dr Arthur Colahan

Upper: horn
Lower: flutes
Pedal: 8'
Drums: 8 beat

3. For the breezes blowing o'er the seas from Ireland
   Are perfumed by the heather as they blow.
   And the women in the uplands diggin' praties,
   Speak a language that the strangers do not know.

4. For the strangers came and tried to teach us their way,
   They scorned us just for being what we are.
   But they might as well go chasing after moonbeams,
   Or light a penny candle from a star.

5. And if there's going to be a life hereafter,
   And somehow I am sure there's going to be,
   I will ask my God to let me make my heaven
   In that dear land across the Irish Sea.

Peg O'My Heart

Words & Music by Bryan & Fisher

Upper: string ensemble
Lower: flutes
Pedal: 8'
Drums: swing

Patsy Fagan (The Dacent Irish Boy)

Words & Music by Thomas P. Keenan

Upper: banjo
Lower: flutes + piano
Pedal: 8'
Drums: march 2/4 or 4/4 (or swing)

2. Now if there's one among you would like to marry me,
   I'll take her to a little home across the Irish Sea.
   I'll dress her up in satin, and please her all I can,
   And let her people see that I'm a dacent Irishman.
      "Hello, Patsy Fagan!" *(etc.)*

3. The day that I left Ireland, 'twas many years ago.
   I left me home in Antrim where the pigs and praties grow.
   But since I left auld Ireland it's always been my plan
   To let the people see that I'm a dacent Irishman.
      "Hello, Patsy Fagan!" *(etc.)*

A Little Bit Of Heaven
(Sure, They Call It Ireland)

Music by Ernest R. Ball
Words by J. Keirn Brennan

Upper: clarinet
Lower: flutes
Pedal: 16' + 8'
Drums: off

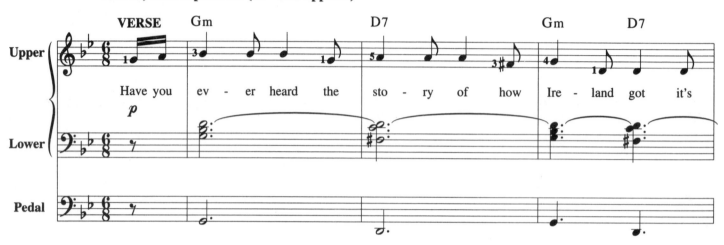

CHORUS

57

Forty Shades Of Green

Words & Music by Johnny Cash

Upper: accordion
Lower: flutes + piano
Pedal: 8'
Drums: swing

miss her lips as soft as ei - der - down.   A -

gain I want to see and do   the   things we've   done and

seen,   where the breeze is sweet as Sha - li - mar,   and there's

for - ty shades of green.   2. I   green

Upper: to accordion

stop drums

61

When Irish Eyes Are Smiling

Words by George Graff & Chauncey Olcott
Music by Ernest Ball

Upper: flute
Lower: flutes
Pedal: 16' + 8'
Drums: waltz

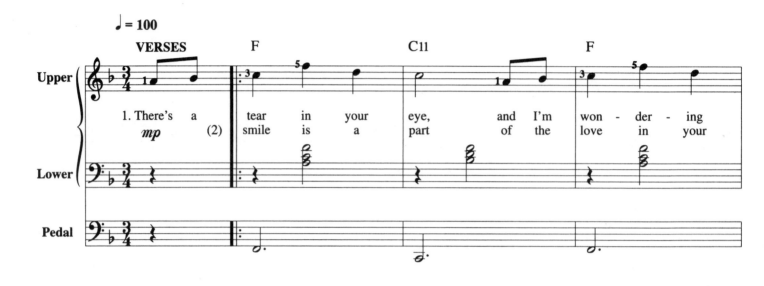

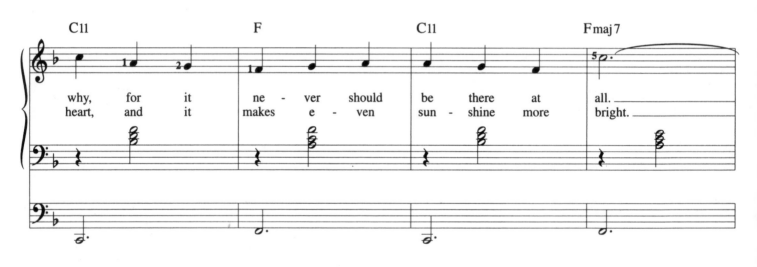

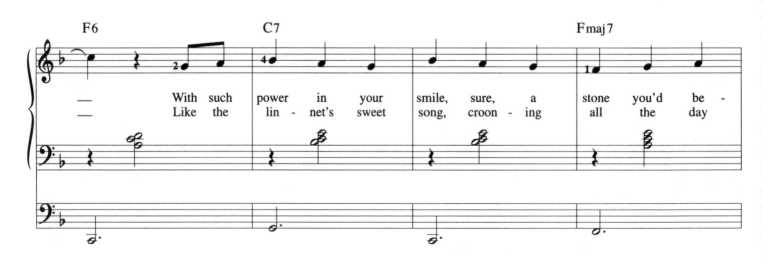

Killarney

Irish Traditional

Upper: string ensemble
Lower: flutes
Pedal: 16' + 8'
Drums: 8 beat (or off)

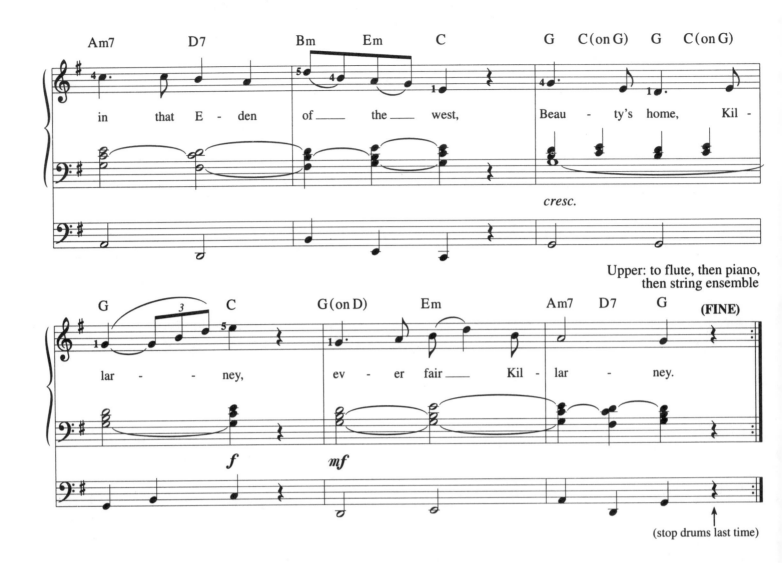

Upper: to flute, then piano,
then string ensemble

cresc.

(FINE)

(stop drums last time)

2. Innisfallen's ruined shrine may suggest a passing sigh;
   But Man's faith can ne'er decline such God's wonders floating by.
   Castle Lough and Glena bay; Mountains Tore and Eagles' Nest.
   Still at Mucross you must pray, tho' the monks are now at rest.
   Angels wonder not that man, there would fain prolong life's span,
   Beauty's home, Killarney, ever fair Killarney.

3. No place else can charm the eye with such bright and varied tints,
   Ev'ry rock that you pass by, verdure broiders or besprints.
   Virgin there the green grass grows, ev'ry morn springs natal day,
   Bright-hued berries daff the snows, smiling Winter's frown away.
   Angels often pausing there doubt if Eden were more fair,
   Beauty's home, Killarney, Heaven's reflex, Killarney.

4. Music there for echo dwells, makes each sound a harmony,
   Many voiced the chorus swells, till it faints in ecstasy.
   With the charmful tints below, seems the heav'n above to vie,
   All rich colours that we know, tinge the cloud-wreath in that sky.
   Wings of angels so might shine, glancing back soft light divine,
   Beauty's home, Killarney, Heaven's reflex, Killarney.

Mick McGilligan's Ball

Words & Music by Michael Casey

Upper: brass ensemble
Lower: flutes + piano
Pedal: 8'
Drums: swing

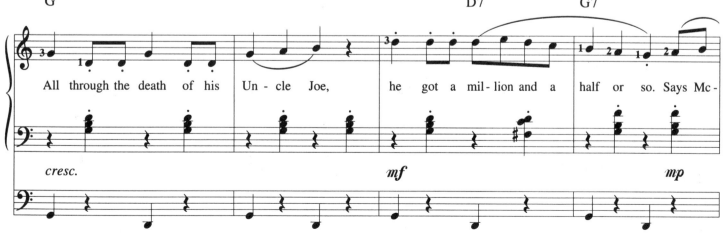

2. All of the neighbours came from near and far, Mulligan arrived there in a motor car.
    Old Missus O'Reilly, bless her heart, came with the fam'ly in a donkey cart.
    Pat O'Rafferty arrived in an aeroplane, you'll never see the like again.
    And there was a shout when two old skins came along at a gallop with two Miss Quinns.
        (to CHORUS)

3. Fluters and fiddlers danced around, drumming on the moleskin made a lovely sound.
    They blew a gale on the old trombone, then reeled and rollick'd to the piper's drone.
    When they'd finished with the whiskey, beer and wine, they rook a hand in "Auld Lang Syne."
    There ne'r was the like, I do declare, as that grand old hooley down in sweet Kildare.
        (to CHORUS)

The Minstrel Boy

Traditional

Upper: oboe
Lower: flutes
Pedal: bass guitar
Drums: 8 beat

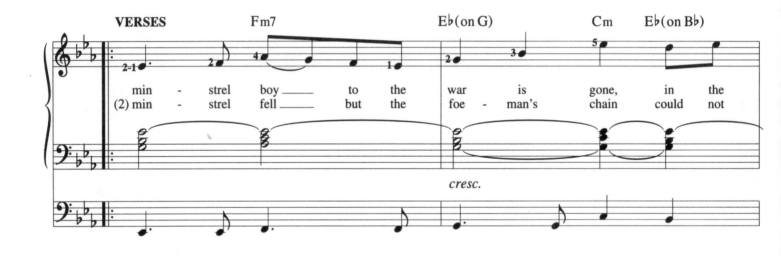

72

MacNamara's Band

Words by John J. Stamford
Music by Shamus O'Connor

Upper: trumpet
Lower: flutes
Pedal: 8'
Drums: march 6/8 (or swing)

2. Whenever an election's on we play on either side,
   The way we play our fine ould airs fills Irish hearts with pride.
   Oh! if poor Tom Moore was living now, he'd make yez understand
   That none could do him justice like ould "Macnamara's Band".
       When the drums go bang, (etc. continuing into CHORUS)

3. We play at wakes and weddings, and at every county ball,
   And at any great man's funeral we play the "Dead March In Saul".
   When the Prince of Wales to Ireland came, he shook me by the hand,
   And said he'd never heard the like of "Macnamara's Band".
       When the drums go bang, (etc. continuing into CHORUS)

Danny Boy

Traditional Irish Melody
Words by Fred E. Weatherly

Upper: string ensemble
Lower: flutes
Pedal: 8'
Drums: 8 beat (or off)